11+ Non-Verbal Reasoning Activity Book

for ages 9-10

This CGP book is bursting with fun-packed
11+ Non-Verbal Reasoning activities for ages 9-10.

It's the perfect way to help them build up their
skills and confidence ahead of the real tests!

Contents

Complete the Pair	2	Puzzle: Prehistoric Adventure	26
Shaded Nets	4	More Cubes and Nets	28
Hidden Shape	6	Odd One Out	30
Rotate the Figure	8	Fold and Punch	32
Cubes and Nets	10	Complete the Grid	34
Find the Figure Like the Others	12	3D Building Blocks	36
2D Views of 3D Shapes	14	Codes	38
Connecting Shapes	16	Different Views of 3D Shapes	40
3D Rotation	18	Fold Along the Line	42
Complete the Series	20	Mixed Practice	44
Reflect the Figure	22		
Complete the Shape	24	Answers	46

Published by CGP

Editors:
Emma Clayton, Rob Hayman, Sharon Keeley-Holden, Luke Molloy, Benedict Robinson, Hannah Roscoe

With thanks to Glenn Rogers for the proofreading.
With thanks to Jan Greenway for the copyright research.

ISBN: 978 1 78908 584 6

Printed by Elanders Ltd, Newcastle upon Tyne.
Clipart from Corel®
Images throughout the book from www.edu-clips.com
Cover design concept by emc design ltd.

Extra copies are available from CGP with next day delivery • 0800 1712 712 • www.cgpbooks.co.uk

About the 11+

The 11+ is an entrance exam

Some schools use the 11+ test to help them decide which students to accept.

There are a few different 11+ test providers, but this book is generic so any student who will one day take an 11+ exam can benefit from it.

The 11+ has four main subjects:

<u>English</u>
Spelling, punctuation, grammar and reading comprehension questions (sometimes there will be a writing task as well).

<u>Maths</u>
Questions can be at the same level as the SATs, or a bit trickier.

<u>Verbal Reasoning</u>
Problem solving and logic using words, letters, etc.

<u>Non-Verbal Reasoning</u>
Problem solving using pictures and symbols.

Papers can be a mix of these subjects or specific to one subject. They may have multiple-choice or write-in questions.

There are lots of ways to prepare for the 11+

Starting preparation early can help children familiarise themselves with 11+ style questions. This gives them time to gradually build their skills as they work towards their test.

Your child may not have come across Non-Verbal Reasoning questions before, so it's completely normal for them to struggle at first. Providing support and encouragement to your child will help if they are finding Non-Verbal Reasoning challenging.

Prioritising subjects or questions that children are finding tricky is a good strategy that will help them improve.

Use a variety of activities to develop skills. Puzzles, like the ones in this book, are a great way to practise 11+ skills without overwhelming children.

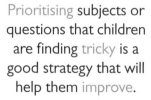

Above all, promote a positive attitude towards the 11+ by offering your child lots of praise and encouragement.

Complete the Pair

How It Works

In a Complete the Pair question, you'll be shown a figure which is then changed in some way to give a second figure. For example:

To answer the question, you'll need to work out how another figure would look if it was changed in the same way.

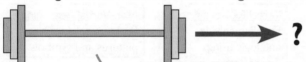
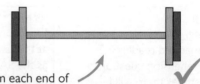

In the example, the third shape disappeared from each end of the pole and the second shape changed from light grey to dark grey.

Now Try These

1. Ella sharpens a yellow pencil and then leaves it on a shelf.

   She does the same to a green pencil. What will the green pencil look like when she leaves it on the shelf?

   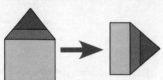
   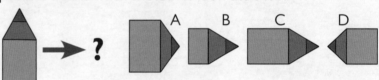

2. To make a children's waffle meal, a cafe makes these changes to an adult's waffle meal:

   adult's meal   children's meal

   They do the same with circular waffles. What will the adult's meal in the box below look like as a children's meal?

   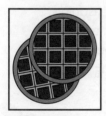
     A
     B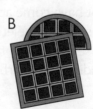
     C
     D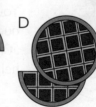
     E

3. Mollie makes some changes to her waistcoat.

   Scott makes the same changes to his waistcoat, so that it now looks like this.

   Draw what Scott's waistcoat used to look like on this figure:

4. Rodney cooks some burgers and sausages on a BBQ for his family.
The figure below shows what the BBQ looks like after 1 minute of cooking and after 10 minutes.

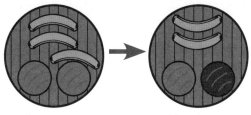

1 minute   10 minutes

Rodney cooks a second portion of sausages and burgers on the BBQ. The figure on the right shows the second portion after 1 minute of cooking.

1 minute

Rodney cooks the second portion in the same way as the first.
What will the BBQ look like after 10 minutes?

A 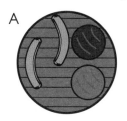   B 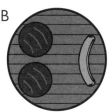   C    D 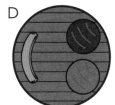   E

5. Catherine rearranges a flower bed, as shown on the right.

She plans to rearrange three other flower beds, A-C, in the same way. Match up these flower beds with what they'll look like after Catherine rearranges them.

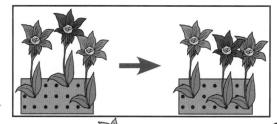

A 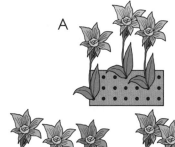   B 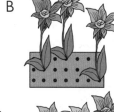   C

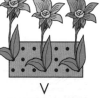      

V   W   X   Y   Z

An Extra Challenge

A scientist has made a machine, the TASTER 5000. When a portion of fruit is put through the TASTER 5000, the machine makes some changes, as shown below.

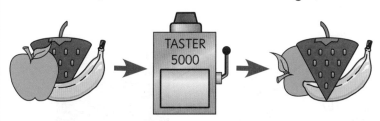

A second portion of fruit, shown in the box, is put through the TASTER 5000. Draw what this portion will look like after the TASTER 5000 has made its changes.

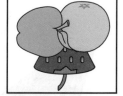

Are you and this page the PAIR-fect match?

3

Shaded Nets

How It Works

In Shaded Nets questions, you'll be given a net and asked to find the 3D shape it makes when it's folded.

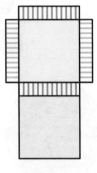 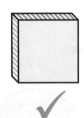 ✓ 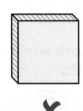 ✗ ✗ ✗

You can use the shadings on the net to work out whether each answer option is correct. In this example, the square faces are yellow and the rectangular faces alternate between having orange stripes and blue stripes. The stripes point towards the square faces.

Now Try These

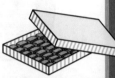

1. Tariq has ordered some parcels online. They all arrive on the same day in almost identical boxes. Tariq wants to open the one containing a DVD first, the net for which is shown below. Which box should he open first?

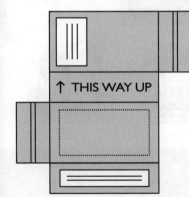

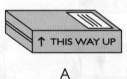

A

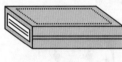

B

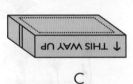

C

D   E   F

2. A chocolatier has designed a box for their newest chocolate bar. The net is shown below. Which of the boxes below has been made using this net?

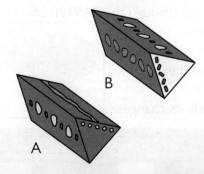

A

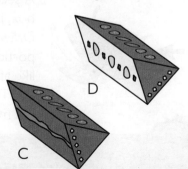

B

C

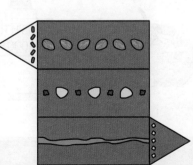

D

3. Melissa is shopping for a locket. She's found one she likes on a jeweller's website and is hoping to find it in their shop. Using the locket's net on the right, work out which of the lockets in the shop window is the one that Melissa wants to buy.

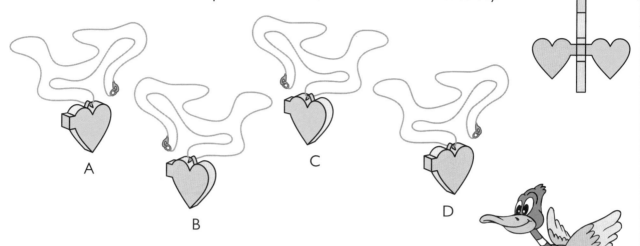

4. Luana has made a 3D shape out of the net below on the right. Use the two views of the shape and the colour key to label the net with the correct layout of colours.

COLOUR KEY

DG — dark green   G — grey
LG — light green   Y — yellow

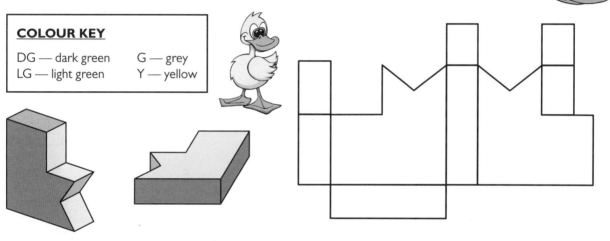

An Extra Challenge

Some honeybees are looking for a specific flower in a garden. The bees know what the petals look like and how they're arranged. Use the net below to figure out which flower the bees are looking for.

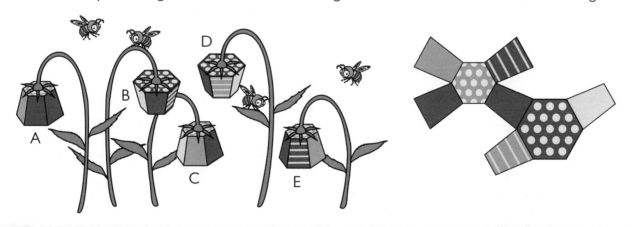

Have you mastered shaded nets or do you need more practice?

Hidden Shape

How It Works

Hidden Shape questions will show you a small shape and ask you to find it within a larger shape. The hidden shape has to be the same size and the same way up as the one that you're shown.

The larger shape will have lots of other shapes and lines inside it too. These might cover part of the small shape.

Now Try These

1. A helicopter pilot is flying over the countryside. She looks down at the landscape below and spots some interesting shapes. Which three of the shapes below can the pilot **not** see?

    A   B   C   D   E   F   G

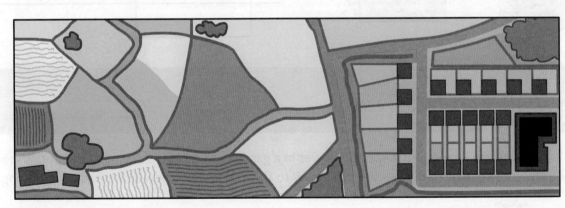

2. Heidi has made a set of four drinks coasters.

    a) In which option can you see the shape on the right?

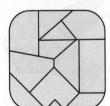 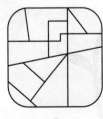  

      A   B   C   D

    b) This shape appears on more than one of the coasters. Which two coasters have this shape?

3. Rajesh and Emily have been icing cupcakes. Each of them signs their cupcakes with a shape that's hidden in the icing. Write the correct letter (R or E) on each cupcake to show who baked it.

Rajesh's shape

Emily's shape

4. Paisley's house has three stained-glass windows. He's drawn a picture of some shapes that can be found in the windows. Using this drawing, find each shape and draw a line around it. There's only one shape to find in each window and each shape only appears once.

An Extra Challenge

Burak has been asked to design a mural for his school. He's drawn lots of different shapes and lines, and he challenges his friends to find the five shapes below. Can you help them find each one? Colour in the shapes once you've found them.

Did you find all the shapes, or are they still hiding from you?

Rotate the Figure

How It Works

Rotate the Figure questions show you a picture and ask you to identify a rotation of it from a set of options. Look carefully at the features of each image.

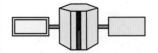  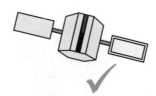 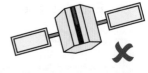

This satellite has been reflected.

This satellite is different from the original figure.

Now Try These

1. Astronaut Axel has got stuck spinning around in space.
   Help rescue him by picking out which of these astronauts is the real Axel.

Axel   A   B   C   D

2. Now Axel is facing in the right direction, he needs to figure out where his spaceship has gone.
   This is what it looks like. Pick out his spaceship from the options below.

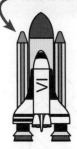  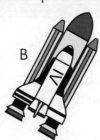 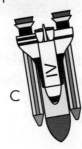 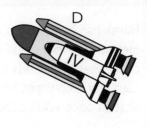

A   B   C   D

3. Axel has received a warning that three identical asteroids are heading directly towards his ship.
   Pick the three asteroids below that match the one on the warning sign.

 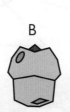 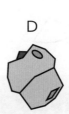

A   B   C   D   E   F

4. Axel has received directions to fly towards this constellation. He can see the constellations below out of the window of his spaceship. Which one should Axel head towards?

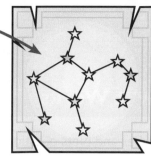

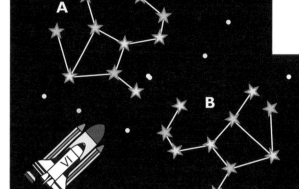

5. Around one of the stars in the constellation are four pairs of matching planets and moons. Use Axel's photographs to match each pair of planets together.

An Extra Challenge

Meanwhile, back on Earth, a UFO is flying around, abducting very specific cows.
Which three of the cows have at least one lightning mark that matches the cow currently being stolen?

Are your rotation skills out of this world?

Cubes and Nets

How It Works

In Cubes and Nets questions, you have to work out which cube can be made from a given net, or which net can be folded to make a given cube.
There are different ways of ruling out the wrong answers. For example:

Which of the cubes can be made from this net?

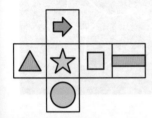

The yellow square should be on the right.

✗

The arrow and the circle should be on opposite sides of the cube.

✗

The arrow should point towards the square.

✗

So this must be the answer. One end of the net wraps around to connect to the other.

✓

Now Try These

1. A takeaway puts food in boxes. The net from which the boxes are made is shown below. Which three boxes on the right can be made from this net?

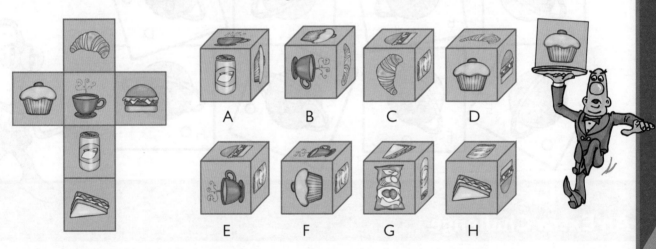

2. Luna, Ahmad and Georgia are deciding what to do today. They make a dice with a possible activity on each face using the net below. Each person rolls the dice. What activity does each person roll?

Luna rolls ....

Ahmad rolls ....

Georgia rolls ....

3. An aquarium gives out surprise gifts in boxes. There are two different nets from which
    the boxes are made. Draw lines to match each box to the net it is made from.

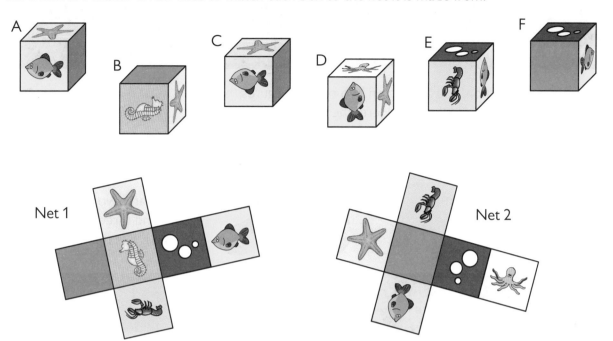

4. Trevor needs to paint the pink droplet shapes on the pale blue faces of the
    cubes below so that they match the net. Which way up should he paint
    each of them? Draw the droplet shapes correctly on the cubes.

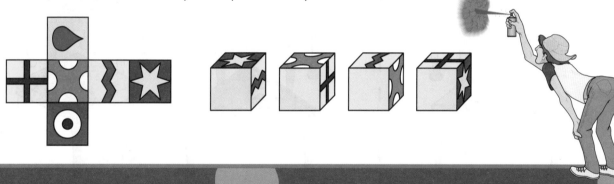

An Extra Challenge

The three blocks below are identical.
Complete the net on the right so that
another identical block can be made.

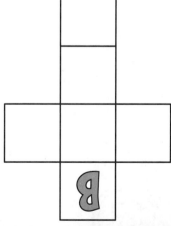

How did you manage when face
to face with Cubes and Nets?

Find the Figure Like the Others

How It Works

In this type of question, you are shown two or three figures that are similar to each other in some way. Here, the number of patches on each sock is one less than the number of lines at the top of that sock.

You then need to pick the figure that's most like them from some options...

There are two patches on this sock and three lines at the top, so it is like the socks above.

Now Try These

1. At the Puzzle Olympics, all of the Olympians must sit at tables that are similar in some way. The two tables on the left are going to be used. Circle the other table which should be used.

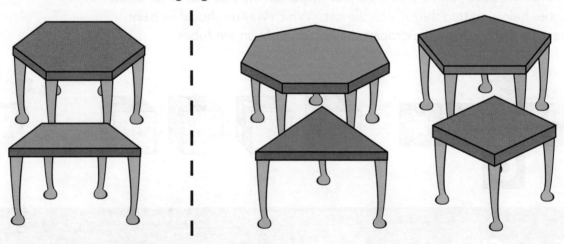

2. The Puzzle Olympic medals are all similar in some way. Which three of the discs on the right are from official Puzzle Olympic medals?

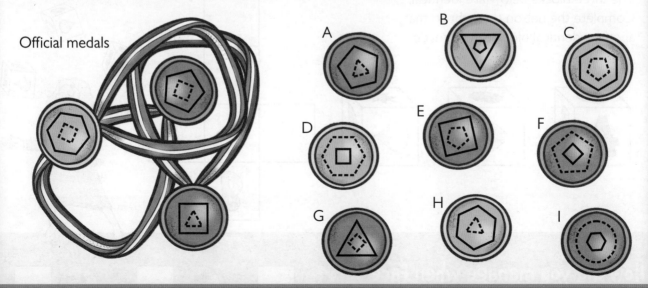

Official medals

3. At the Puzzle Olympics, each Olympian must choose a stationery set that is arranged in the correct way. Which stationery set looks the most like the ones in the box?

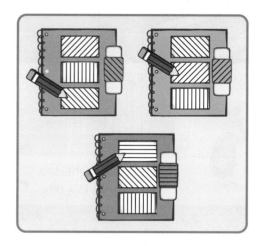

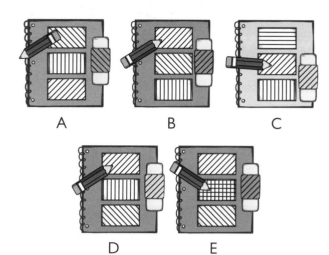

A   B   C

D   E

4. It is snack time at the Puzzle Olympics. First the gingerbread people must be sorted into families of four. Draw a line from each family to **one** gingerbread person to complete the family.

An Extra Challenge

The words below all have something in common.
Hint: It isn't about what the words mean.

| almost | ghost | ace | forty | chimps |

Which of the words below also has this feature?

| end | begin | start | middle |

2D Views of 3D Shapes

How It Works

In these questions, you'll be given a 3D shape and asked what it looks like in 2D from a certain direction.

From the right, the snail looks like this.

Now Try These

1. Misaki's grandma has given her an antique teapot.
   Which of these 2D views shows what Misaki's teapot looks like from the right?

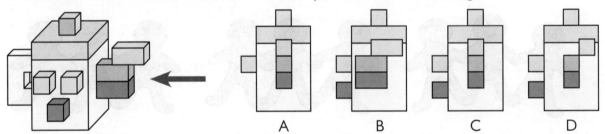

   A   B   C   D

2. Jack has picked up four new books from the book fair.
   What would Jack's stack of books look like from the left?

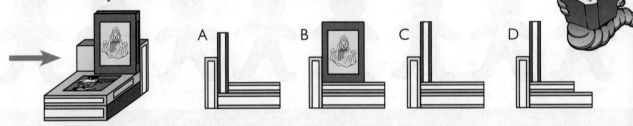

   A   B   C   D

3. Connor and Ezra are on holiday together, but they've managed to lose each other.
   Connor thinks that they are on opposite sides of this square.
   How will the square look to Ezra if he is standing at the back of it?

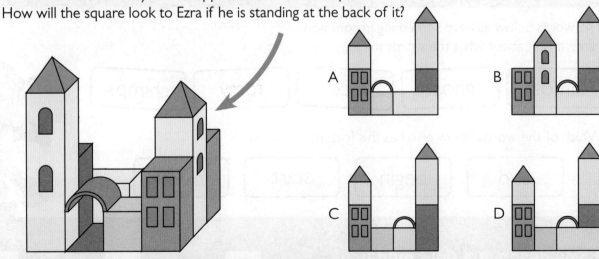

   A   B

   C   D

4. Amanpreet flies a drone over his local stadium.
   Which view (A, B, C or D) shows what the stadium will look like from above?

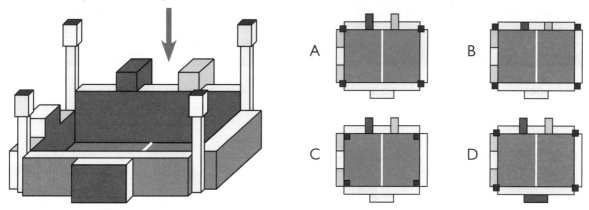

A   B

C   D

5. Naomi has built a new climbing frame for the monkeys at the zoo.
   Which of the options below matches how the climbing frame would look from the right?

A   B

C   D

An Extra Challenge

Rosie has spent all afternoon building a sandcastle on the beach.
Use the grid below to draw what Rosie's sandcastle looks like from above.
Write a letter F on the squares where the flags should be.

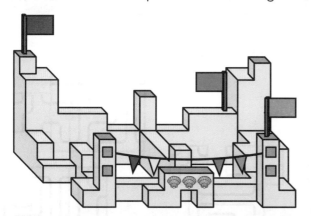

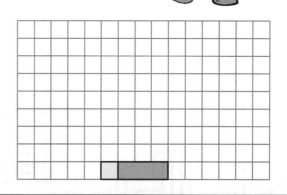

How did you do with
these 2D views?

Connecting Shapes

How It Works

In these questions you will be shown a set of shapes with some sides labelled by letters. You need to connect the shapes together so that sides with the same letter join up.

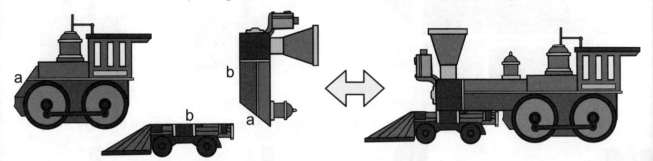

Think carefully about your answers — you'll have to rotate some of the shapes to connect them together, and matching sides might not be the same length.

Now Try These

1. Lucia is building a model rocket. The pieces are labelled to show how to connect them together. Circle what the rocket will look like when she's finished.

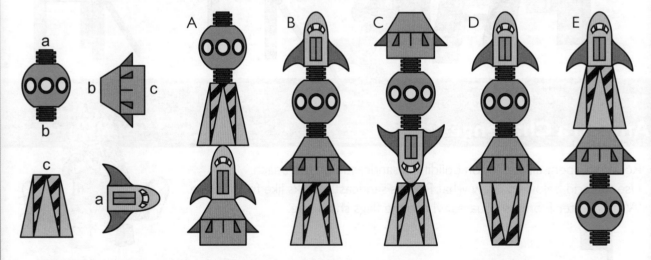

2. Ellie the electrician is trying to fix some wires, but the instructions are all torn up. Circle the repaired set of instructions.

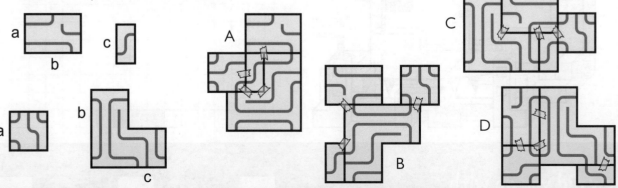

3. Varsha is sewing a patchwork blanket. Using the pictures in the thought bubbles, label the correct sides of the fabric pieces with letters to show how they should be sewn together.

4. Mark broke his toy starfish into pieces. The pieces are shown below on the right.
   Label the correct sides of the pieces with letters to show how they should be stuck back together.

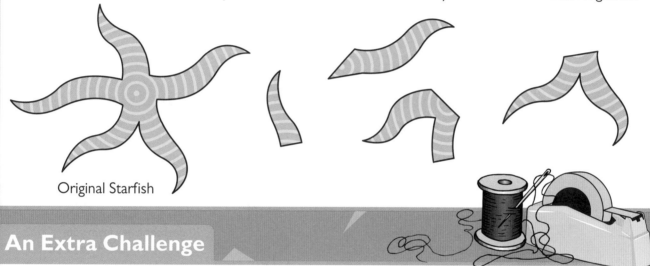

Original Starfish

An Extra Challenge

Ross is helping his dad to build a den in the back garden, but they can't work out how the pieces are meant to fit together. Finish the picture below of what the completed den should look like.

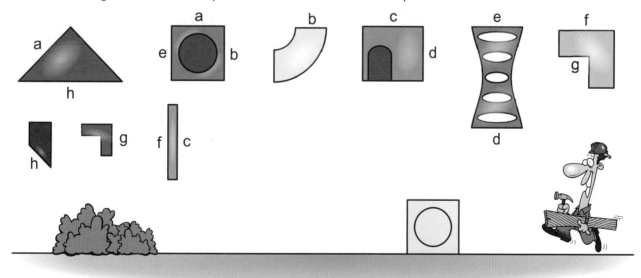

Did everything come together properly?

3D Rotation

How It Works

In these questions, you'll be asked to work out what a 3D shape will look like after it has been rotated. There are several ways that a shape can be rotated:

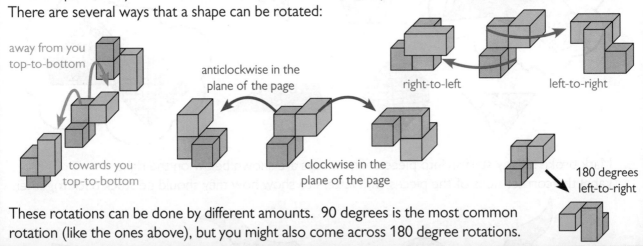

away from you
top-to-bottom

towards you
top-to-bottom

anticlockwise in the
plane of the page

clockwise in the
plane of the page

right-to-left

left-to-right

180 degrees
left-to-right

These rotations can be done by different amounts. 90 degrees is the most common rotation (like the ones above), but you might also come across 180 degree rotations.

Now Try These

1. Victor and Gemima each glue three boxes together. They then play a game where they try to draw what each set of boxes will look like after its been rotated in a certain way. Decide who has the correct answer in each case below.

a) 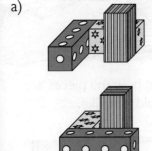 When this set of boxes is rotated 90 degrees left-to-right, it will look like...

b) When this set of boxes is rotated 90 degrees away from you, top-to-bottom, it will look like...

Victor's answer   Gemima's answer

 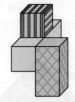

Victor's answer   Gemima's answer

2. Nacho the hamster will only eat pieces of food that are a particular shape. Using the 3D shape on the right to help you, circle the pieces of food that Nacho will eat.

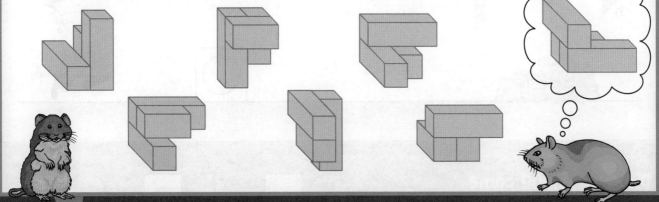

3. a) Four sea otters are playing together. Each otter has its own special rock that it likes
       to play with. The otters drop the rocks in the water and then swim around, trying to
       catch them. Draw lines to match each otter's rock to its rotated version below.

   Oscar's rock   Opal's rock   Otto's rock   Olive's rock

              A   B   C   D

   b) The otters have also thrown sticks into the water to catch.
       Which of the options below matches the stick on the left?

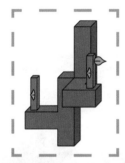 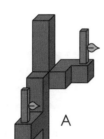   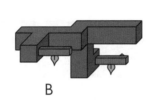 

              A   B   C   D

An Extra Challenge

A digger clears away the following pieces of rubble from a building site:

Which of the options below can be made by rotating a piece of this rubble
90 degrees right-to-left, and then 90 degrees towards you, top-to-bottom?

     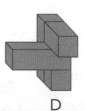 

        A   B   C   D

**Has all this rotation left
you feeling dizzy?**

Complete the Series

How It Works

All the figures in a Complete the Series question follow a pattern. Work out what is changing from one figure to the next and identify the figure that is missing from the series. For example:

The elephants in this series rotate 45 degrees clockwise and alternate between purple and yellow...

...So the missing elephant must look like this:

You might also come across series that are made up of pairs of figures, like this:

Look at how the first figure changes to become the second figure and make the same changes to the third figure.

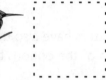

The bird turns yellow and is reflected, so the answer is this:

Now Try These

1. Some freckled forest frogs line up on a riverbank to form a series. Which frog (A, B, C or D) should come next in the series?

2. These snakes all slither along in a series. Which of the snakes on the right would complete this series?

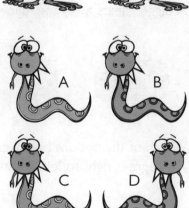

3. Marcus the monkey has found a bunch of rare bananas. These bananas always grow in a series.

Draw the banana that would come fourth in this bunch:

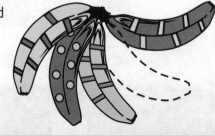

4. All of the tigers in a family form a series. The first three tigers in the series are shown on the right.
Circle the tigers below that are part of the same family.

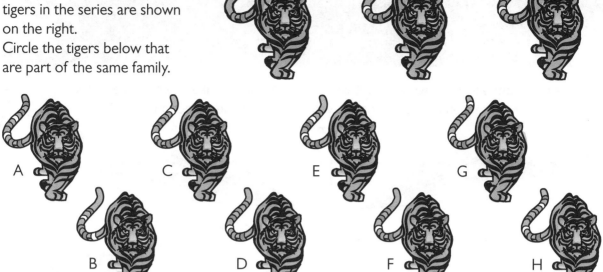

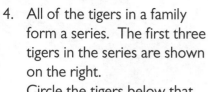

A   C   E   G

B   D   F   H

5. Even the trees in this jungle grow in a series.

?

Which tree should come fourth in this series? Circle the correct one below.

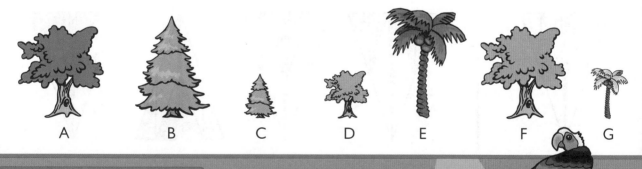

A   B   C   D   E   F   G

An Extra Challenge

The colourful leaves on this tropical vine grow in a specific series.
Draw the next four leaves in the series.

Did you have lots of fun-gle with this jungle page?

21

Reflect the Figure

How It Works

In these questions you need to work out what a figure will look like when it is reflected over a line. The direction of the mirror line will affect what the reflection looks like.

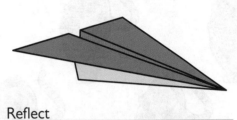

Reflect

Reflect

This image has been reflected in the vertical mirror line.

This image has been reflected in the horizontal mirror line.

Now Try These

1. Alisha has designed a paper plane for a competition. The design is a reflection of the plane on the left. Circle the plane below which is Alisha's.

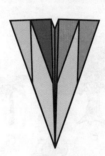 Reflect 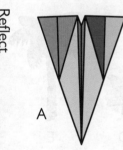 A 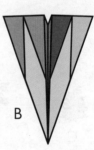 B 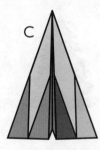 C 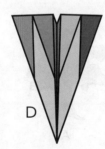 D

2. Gary's plane looks like a downwards reflection of the plane in the box. Circle the plane below which is Gary's.

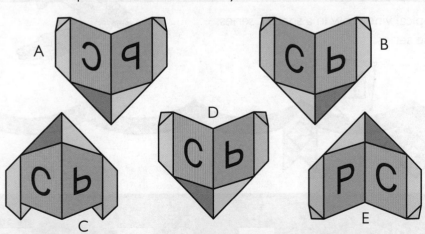

A   B   D   C   E

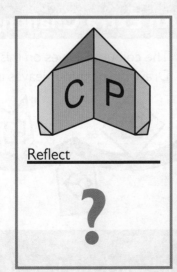

Reflect

?

3. Each person in Rani's team has a pair of paper planes, which are reflections of each other when arranged as shown on the right. The team all throw their planes at once. Draw lines to match up the pairs of planes and find which plane is the odd one out.

Reflect _____

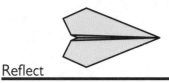

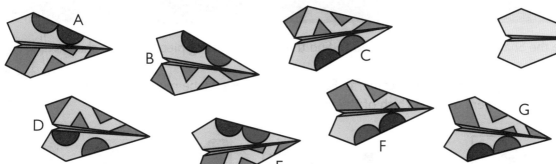

4. One of the team's planes has gone missing. It should look like a reflection of the odd one out above. Draw the missing plane on the template to the right.

5. Dominic has made the plane on the left below.
   What would the plane look like if it was reflected over the line?

Reflect _____

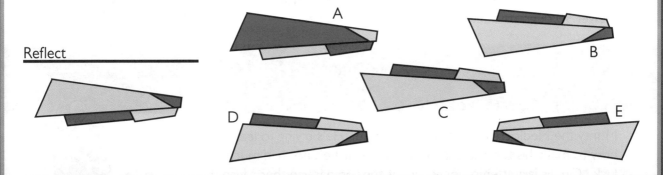

An Extra Challenge

Miranda is making a parachute for one of her toys. She wants it to be a reflection of a design she made earlier. She draws the green shape, then forgets which line she was reflecting in. Work out whether she was reflecting in a vertical or horizontal mirror line, and finish the parachute for her.

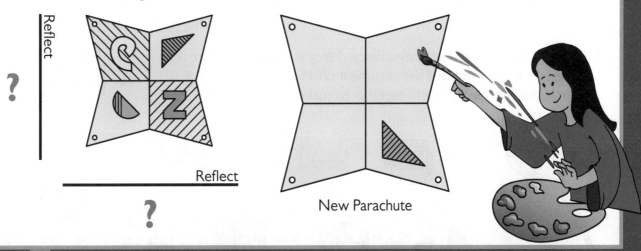

Reflect

?

Reflect

?

New Parachute

Were you flying high with these questions?

Complete the Shape

How It Works

Complete the Shape questions will ask you to find the correct missing piece of a 3D shape.

Francesca has bought herself a new camera. Before she can use it, she needs to fit the lens piece to the camera body. Which of the lens pieces below is the correct one?

complete camera

camera body

The missing piece won't always be the same way round as it is on the complete shape. In this example, you have to rotate the answer 90 degrees clockwise in the plane of the page.

Now Try These

1. Monty the Mediocre is an average magician. He's trying to learn how to make his top hat disappear, but so far he's not had much luck. On his last attempt, only part of the top hat vanished. Use the pictures of the top hat below to work out which part went missing.

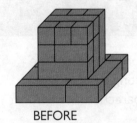

BEFORE

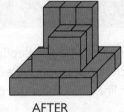

AFTER

A

B

C

D

2. Monty has a pet parakeet called Percy. Percy is very good at breaking things. He's just knocked this ornament off Monty's mantelpiece. Circle the two pieces that fit together to make the ornament.

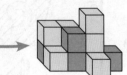

3. A builder is doing some work on an old house. There's a fireplace in the front room that needs repairing. Which two pieces below does the builder need to use to complete the fireplace?

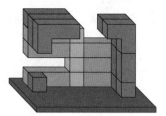

A

B

C

D

E

F

4. Nina works at an aquarium. It's her job to feed Sharky the shark. She lowers a large chunk of meat into his tank.

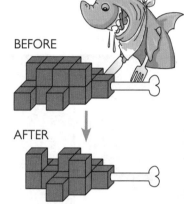
BEFORE

AFTER

a) Sharky takes a bite and swims away. What does this bite look like? Use the before and after pictures to help you.

A

B

C

D

b) Sharky comes back to take another bite. Which of the options below shows what the chunk of meat looks like after this second bite? Use the pictures in part a) to help you.

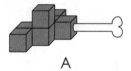
A

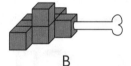
B

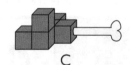
C

Sharky's second bite

An Extra Challenge

A scientist is doing some experiments. She is testing crystals which all start like this.
She hits four crystals with a hammer to see how much breaks off each one.
Match up the two pieces of each smashed crystal.

experiment 1

experiment 2

experiment 3

experiment 4

How well do you think your skills are shaping up?

Prehistoric Adventure

Ruth's friend Sydney has become stranded in prehistoric times! Ruth has travelled back in time to find him and bring him back to the present day. What challenges could lie ahead?

1. It's not long before Ruth finds one of Sydney's camps. There are pieces of paper everywhere! Ruth knows that Sydney likes to fold his maps in a particular way. If she can find his map, perhaps it will tell her where he is stranded. Circle the piece of paper that is folded in the correct way.

Sydney folds maps like this:

A

B

C

D

E

2. On the back of the map is some kind of series. Ruth thinks it will give her the coordinates of Sydney's location. Can you complete the pattern to work out the coordinates?

3. The coordinates lead down a river. Ruth needs to build a raft in order to travel down the river. Write letters next to the sides of the pieces below to show how Ruth can combine them to make the raft in the bubble. Sides that join up should have the same letter.

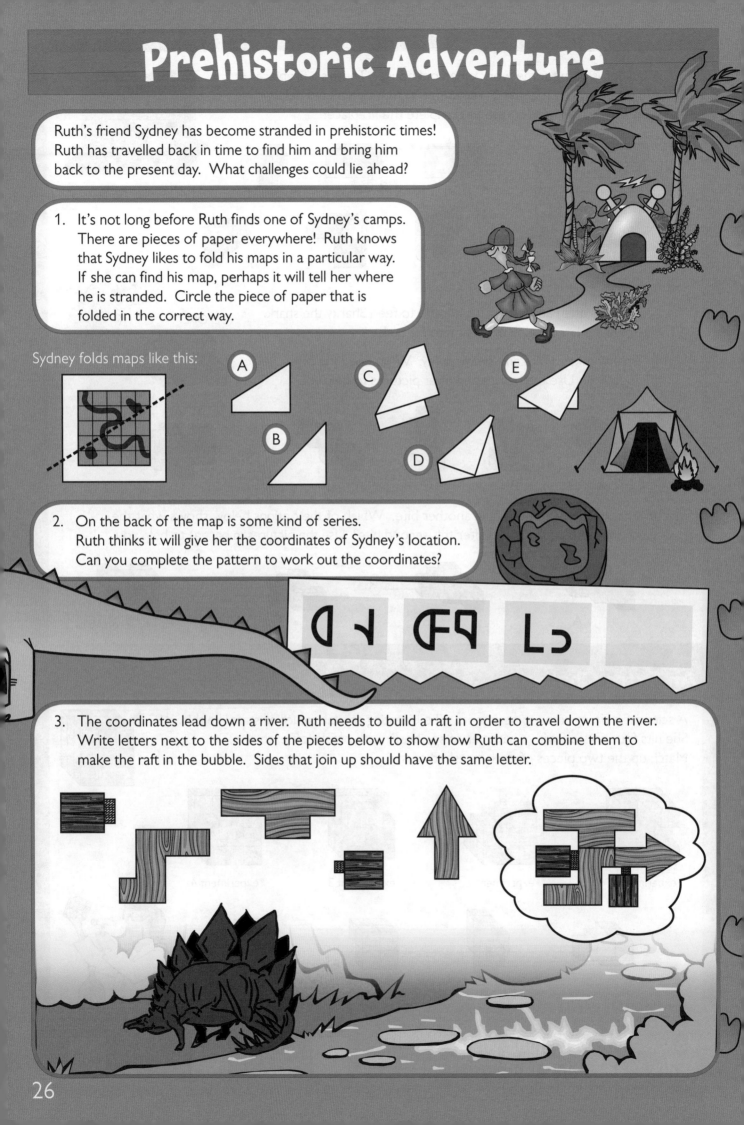

4. Ruth rows down the river for many hours. She needs to come to shore just after a particular tree, which she has seen on the map. Circle what the tree will look like when it is reflected in the river.

The tree on the map:

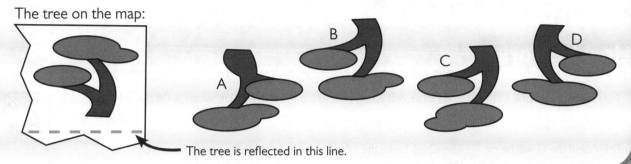

The tree is reflected in this line.

5. It's getting dark. Ruth needs to pitch her tent so she can go to bed. Which of the nets below could be folded into the correct tent?

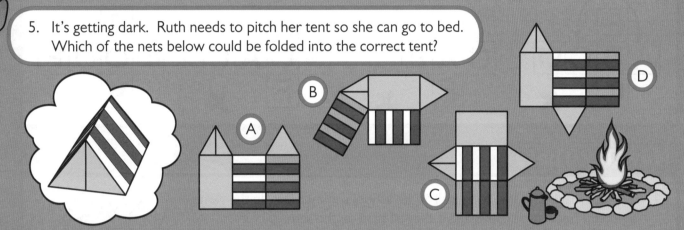

6. That night, Ruth hears some noises in the bushes. Could it be a dinosaur? She can scare it away by shining her torch at it. Colour in the dinosaur shape so she knows where it is.

7. The next morning, Ruth goes out to find Sydney, but there is one last obstacle. The map shows that Sydney is stranded next to a certain rock formation, but she can't work out which one it is. Circle the correct rock formation so she can finally make it to Sydney.

The rock formation looks like this from above...

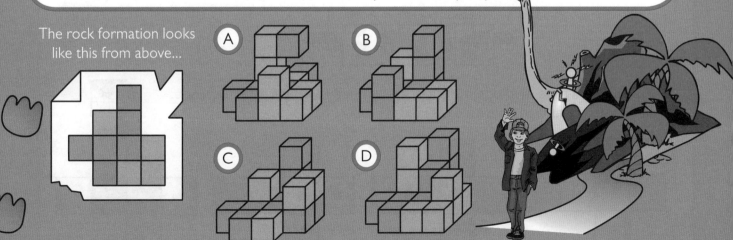

Thanks for your help! Sydney has a few scrapes and bruises, but all he wants now is a nice cup of tea...

27

More Cubes and Nets

How It Works

You have to work out what a cube will look like for a given net, or what a net will look like for a given cube. For example, which net below folds to make the cube on the right?

The A and the C will be on opposite sides using this net.

The C will be to the left of the upright A using this net.

The wrong side of the E will be closest to the A using this net.

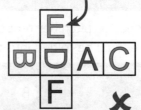

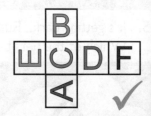

Now Try These

1. Zahra is making a game for a stall at the school summer fair. In the game, a person spins three cubes and if they all stop on the same picture, they win a prize. Zahra uses the three nets below to make the cubes.

Win!

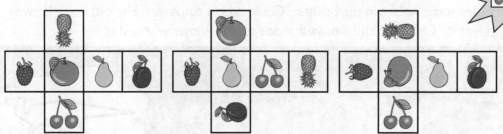

She puts the cubes onto a stick in a random order.
Which option below could show Zahra's three cubes?

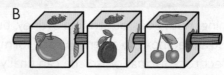

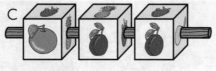

2. Fred makes a cube which looks like a face when viewed from a particular angle. Which net might Fred have used to make the cube?

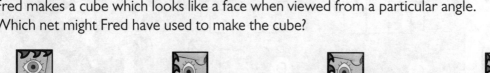

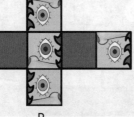

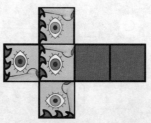

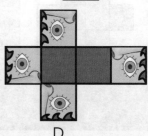

A   B   C   D

3. a) A pet farm is making dice for children to roll to decide which animal they'll visit first.
   The nets below make two slightly different dice. Decide which nets make the same dice.

A

B

C

D

E

F

Nets .... , ... and .... make the same dice.   Nets .... , ... and .... make the same dice.

b) Here are both dice that can be made from the nets.
   Name the animal that is missing from each dice.

....

....

An Extra Challenge

The three diagrams on the right show different views of the same cube. Complete the nets below so that they will all make this cube when folded.

Odd One Out

How It Works

Odd One Out questions ask you to find the figure that is <u>most unlike</u> the others.
There could be many differences between each figure, but look carefully and you'll see that <u>all but one</u> of the figures have something in common — so the one that doesn't have it is the odd one out.

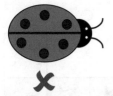 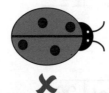  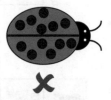

Here, all the ladybirds have a different total number of spots, so this difference won't help you find the odd one out. However, <u>all but one</u> of the ladybirds have the same number of spots on each side of their body, so the ladybird with a different number of spots on each side is the odd one out.

Now Try These

1. A sailor is going on a voyage to France and needs a working compass for the journey.
    Although the sailor owns the five compasses below, four of them are broken.

    The working compass is the one that is most unlike the others.
    Which compass will get the sailor to France?

A   B   C   D   E

2. Geoffrey owns five different hats, A-E. He needs to choose one of his hats to wear to a wedding.
    Geoffrey picks the hat that is most unlike the others. Which hat does he wear to the wedding?

A   B   C   D   E

3. A scientist takes five photographs of shooting stars. Afterwards, the scientist spills coffee on the photograph that is most unlike the others. Which photograph did the scientist spill coffee on?

A   B   C   D   E

4. Rachel pulls out a drawer and finds some stamps, scissors and batteries.
   For each type of object, circle the one most unlike the others of that type.

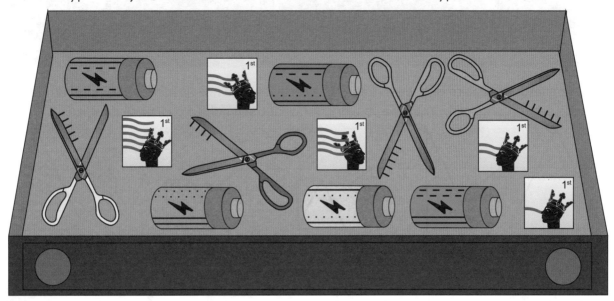

5. Mrs Ferris is looking at the five doughnuts below in a bakery.
   She buys the doughnut which is most unlike the others. Which one does she buy?

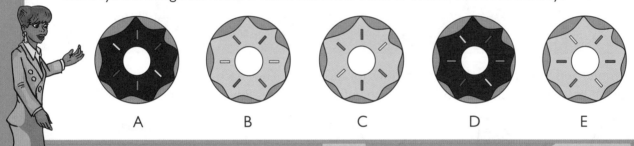

A   B   C   D   E

An Extra Challenge

Brendon has four different maps of a zoo. The correct map is the one that is
most unlike the others. Use the directions shown below, along with the correct map,
to state which direction Brendon should go if he wants to find the zebras.

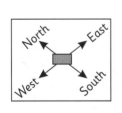

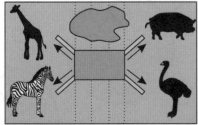

Direction to
the zebras:

· · · · · · · · · · · · · · · · · · · ·

Have you any doubt that you
can find the odd one out?

Fold and Punch

How It Works

In these questions, a piece of paper is folded in a certain way, a hole is punched (or cut) into it, then the paper is unfolded. You have to work out what the unfolded paper will look like.

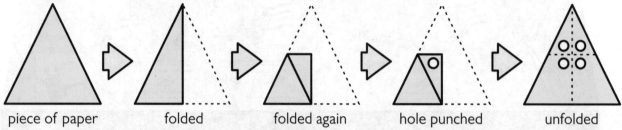

piece of paper   folded   folded again   hole punched   unfolded

Make sure you follow the folds carefully to work out which parts of the paper the hole will go through.

Now Try These

1. Raymond and Shazia are making decorations for a parade. They each fold a paper circle twice, then cut holes in it. Can you work out which unfolded shape is Raymond's and which is Shazia's?

Raymond's Design

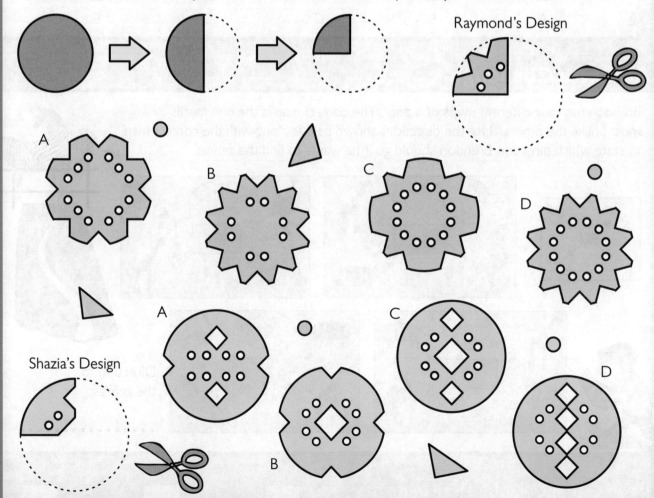

A   B   C   D

Shazia's Design

A   C   D   B

2. Jordan is making a light show for the parade. He folds two pieces of paper, punches three holes in each of them and then unfolds them to get patterns to shine lights through.

How Jordan folded each piece of paper is shown below, along with the patterns of holes he made. The folded pieces of paper are shown next to each pattern.
Draw the punched holes in the correct places on the folded pieces of paper.

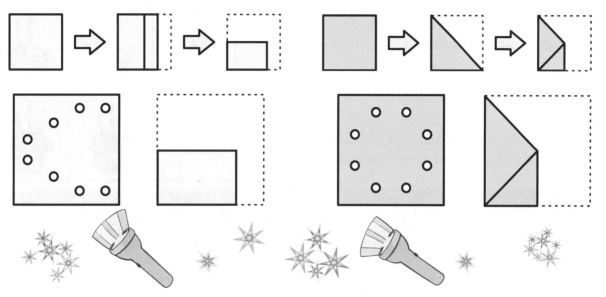

3. Sarah is also making decorations for the parade. She folds some paper three times, then cuts a triangular hole in it, as shown below.

hole

What will the paper look like when Sarah unfolds it?

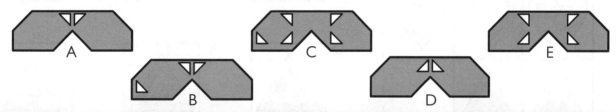

An Extra Challenge

Imelda has made a puzzle. When a square of paper is folded and punched as shown below, it will unfold to give a pattern of holes. Placing the unfolded paper over the grid of letters will reveal a hidden word. Can you work out what the hidden word is?

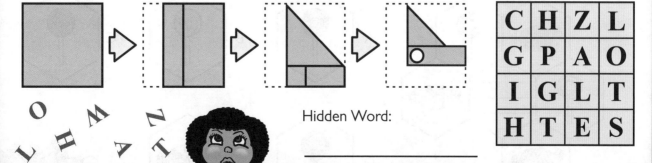

Hidden Word:

_____

C	H	Z	L
G	P	A	O
I	G	L	T
H	T	E	S

How did you find these questions?

33

Complete the Grid

How It Works

You need to choose the figure that best fits into a grid containing a pattern.

Grids can come in different shapes and sizes, including squares and hexagons.

In this grid, working from left to right, the colours of the sprinkles swap round and a new candle is added.

Now Try These

1. Maisie has bought a new board game which involves stacking counters on top of each other. Which of the squares on the right would complete this grid?

 A

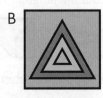 B

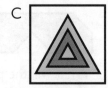 C

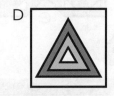 D

 E

 F

2. Ailsa is in a sweet shop where all the sweets are kept in hexagonal jars. Some of the jar lids are arranged in the grid shown below. What would the missing lid look like?

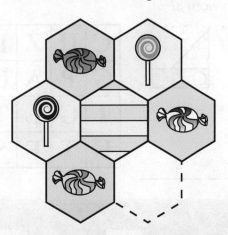

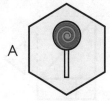 A

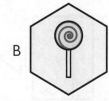 B

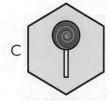 C

 D

 E

3. Henry is tiling his bathroom floor, but he is unsure where one of the tiles should go. Which grid below can be completed using the tile on the left? You don't need to rotate the tile.

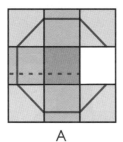
A

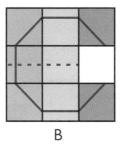
B

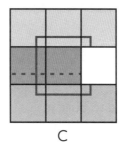
C

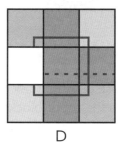
D

4. a) Some brave knights are getting ready for a feast. Before they start, they hang their shields up to form a grid. However, Sir Prise is missing, so they leave a space for his shield.

Which of the options below is Sir Prise's shield?

A

B

C

D

E

F

b) Three more knights show up and add their shields in a new row at the bottom of the grid. Pick the three shields below that can be put in order to match the grid.

An Extra Challenge

Jasmine makes her own jigsaw pieces. She plans for her jigsaw pieces to fit together to form a patterned grid.

When she puts the pieces together, as shown on the right, she notices that two of the pieces contain mistakes, so they don't follow the pattern correctly.

Given that the first column is correct, find the two pieces that don't follow the pattern correctly and suggest what they should look like.

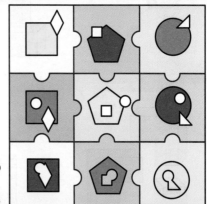

Have you got a big grin after finishing these grid questions?

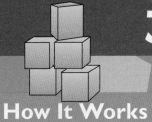

3D Building Blocks

How It Works

These questions ask you to match an object with the set of blocks used to build it. The blocks won't always be the right way round, like the blocks shown on the right.

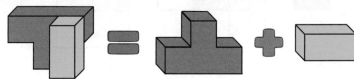

Some blocks might not be fully visible in the object, so you'll have to think carefully about the different shapes each block could be.
For example, this object could be made up from either of the sets of blocks on the right.

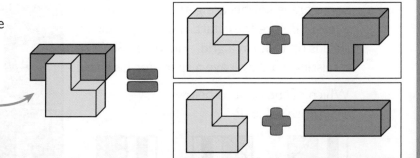

Now Try These

1. Oscar paints four wooden blocks and uses them to make a funny-looking duck. Which block below does Oscar <u>not</u> use to build the duck?

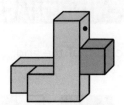

A

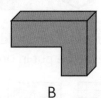

B

C

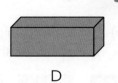

D

2. Biyu has four sets of blocks, A-D. She uses three of the sets of blocks to build three different structures, **X**, **Y** and **Z**. Match up each structure with the set of blocks it was built from.

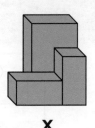

X

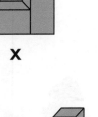

Y

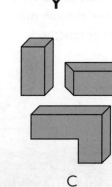

Z

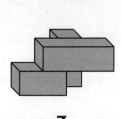

A

B

C

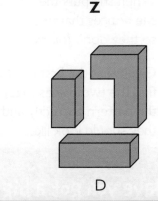

D

3. Raisa builds some artistic wooden stands. She uses four types of block, A-D, shown below. How many of each block does she use to build all the stands below?

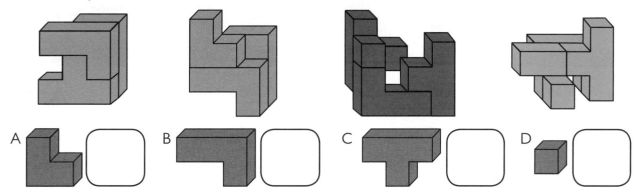

A   B   C   D

4. Ed takes apart an old wall and plans to use its pieces to build a new wall. Which two of the walls below could Ed build using the pieces from the old wall?

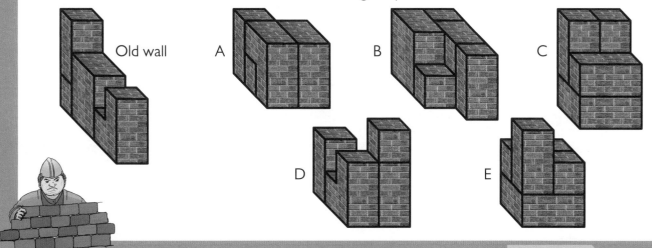

Old wall   A   B   C

D   E

An Extra Challenge

a) A statue is shown below from the front and back. It is made from four types of block, A-D. How many of block A must be in the statue?

front: back: A   B   C   D

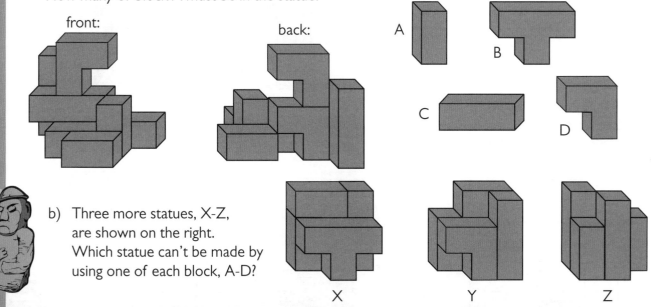

b) Three more statues, X-Z, are shown on the right. Which statue can't be made by using one of each block, A-D?

X   Y   Z

Is this the topic you were built for?

37

Codes

How It Works

You will be shown some figures, each labelled with code letters. You need to work out what the code letters mean.

Here, **E** = solid lines, **F** = dotted lines and **G** = dashed lines. And then, **Y** = horizontal lines and **Z** = vertical lines.

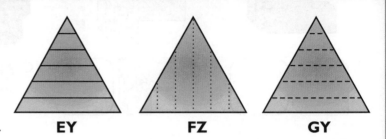

EY   FZ   GY

Then you'll be given a fourth figure, not labelled with code letters. You have to work out the code for it.

This figure has dashed lines (code letter **G**) and vertical lines (code letter **Z**). So its code is **GZ**.

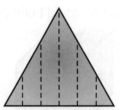

EY	GZ
GY	EZ

Now Try These

Leroy is an explorer. He visits an ancient tomb to find the "lost treasure of Basktiki".
He knows that a series of booby traps and coded doors lie between him and the treasure.

1. To enter the tomb, Leroy must say the code of the figure on the door out loud. What should he say to enter the tomb?

   KU   **KX**   **KV**

   JW   **JX**

JU   JV   KW

2. At the next door, Leroy finds five buttons.
   Leroy's notes on the left show some symbols labelled with codes.
   He knows that the button with code **NS** opens this door. Circle this button.

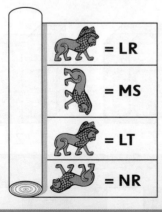

= LR

= MS

= LT

= NR

3. Walking through the door activates cursed ancient mummies!
They advance on Leroy, who sees a new code on the wall beside him.

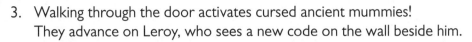

= CP   = DQ   = CR   = EP

Leroy works out that the mummies can be deactivated if he presses the code for the figure shown on the right. Circle this code.

EQ   ER   DR

CP   CQ

4. After deactivating the mummies, Leroy sees a trapdoor.

To open the trapdoor, Leroy must etch the correct 3-letter code into the centre of the door. What is the correct 3-letter code?

___ ___ ___

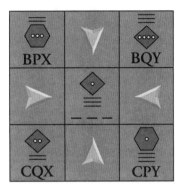

BPX   BQY

CQX   CPY

ahhhh!

5. Leroy falls through the trapdoor and lands in the resting place of Queen Basktiki.
Within her casket, behind the central stone, lies the lost treasure of Basktiki.
All Leroy has to do is write the correct code above the central stone and the casket will open.

| CRV | DSW | _ _ _ | DRW | DSV |

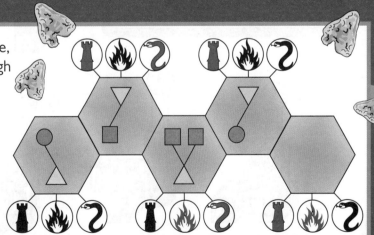

Can you solve the final code and retrieve the treasure?   ___ ___ ___

An Extra Challenge

Immediately after Leroy picks up the treasure, the tomb begins to crumble. He runs through the falling rubble and finds a secret passage.

The passage contains the tomb's most ancient code, shown on the right. Solving the code will open the end of the passage and help Leroy escape the tomb.

Draw the correct pattern on the final hexagonal stone to escape the tomb.

Did you escape the tomb or meet your doom?

 ☐   ☐   ☐

Different Views of 3D Shapes

How It Works

In these questions, you'll be given a 3D figure and asked what it looks like from a certain direction.

To the man on the left, the diving tower looks like this:

To the girl in the rubber ring, it looks like this:

Now Try These

1. In a computer game, Muscle Man must guard the legendary Marble Orb from Dragon Dude. The players controlling the characters see the game world from above.
   Which view does Muscle Man, Dragon Dude and a player have of the structure shown?

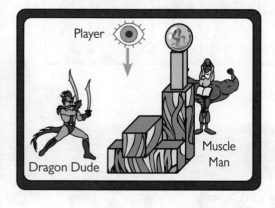

A

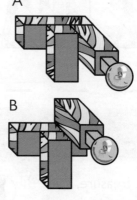

B

C   D

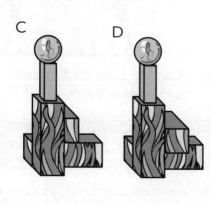

E   F   G   H   I

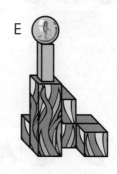    

Muscle Man sees view ....   Dragon Dude sees view ....   The player sees view ....

2. Lasso Lucy is trying to lasso the rock formation below.
   Which option shows Lucy's view of the rock formation?

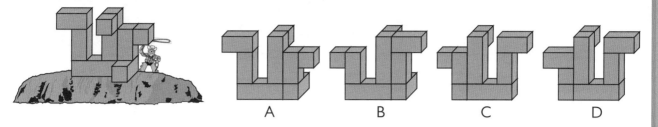

A   B   C   D

3. Cowboy Carl is galloping through the desert. He sees each of the cacti below from the left.
   Draw lines to match each of the four cacti to Carl's view of it.

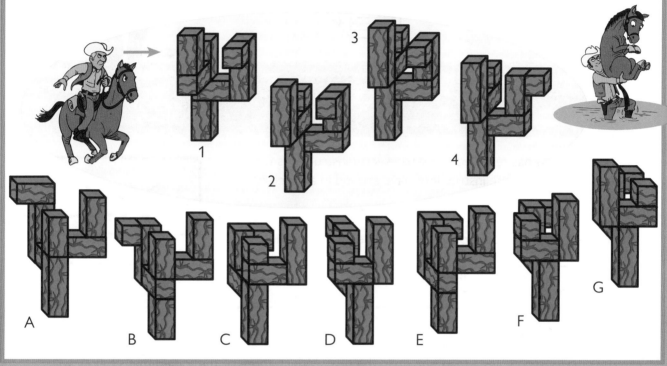

1   2   3   4

A   B   C   D   E   F   G

An Extra Challenge

Daisy the duckling is hiding under a glass coffee table. There is a sculpture standing on the coffee table above her. What does the sculpture look like to Daisy?

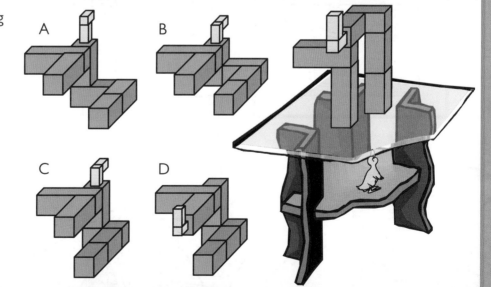

A   B   C   D

Did you work out how things look from different points?

41

Fold Along the Line

How It Works

Fold Along the Line questions ask you to work out what a shape will look like after it is folded along a line.

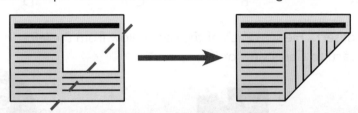

Now Try These

1. Sergio the spy has received some top secret instructions for his next mission. The instructions have arrived in a specially folded envelope.

   How will the envelope look when it is folded along this line?

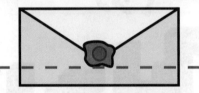

 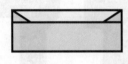 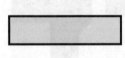 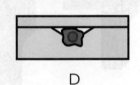

   A   B   C   D

2. The envelope contains a map, shown in the box. Which three of the folded maps below will be the same size and shape as Sergio's map when unfolded? Each map was folded once.

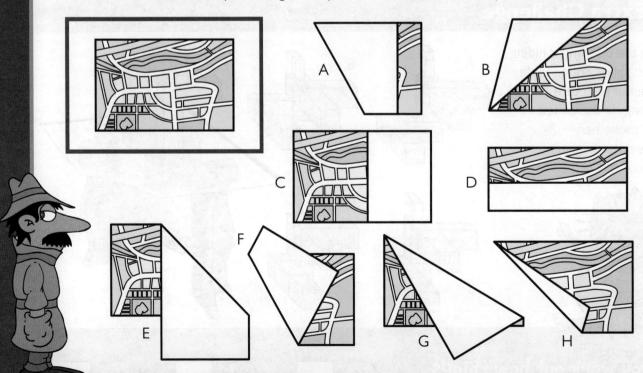

3. Every spy knows that they need their long coat before they can do any spying. Which of the options below shows the lines that Sergio's coat (shown on the left) has been folded along?

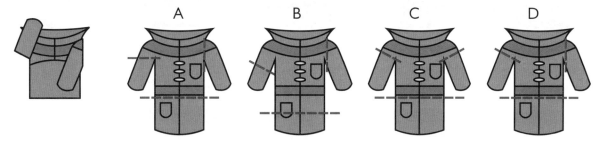

A   B   C   D

4. Sergio has folded up his ID card in a specific pattern.
   Which of the options below matches the order in which Sergio has folded his card?

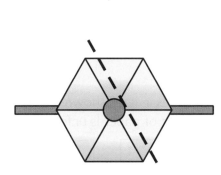

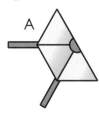

A

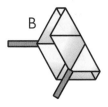

B

C

5. Sergio also folds a parachute into his backpack.
   How will the parachute look if Sergio folds it along the dotted line?

A   B   C

    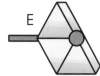   

D   E   F

An Extra Challenge

After speaking to a fellow spy in a cafe, Sergio was given a strange note with symbols on both sides. How will the note look if Sergio folds it along the two orange dotted lines?

Front

Back

A

B

C

D

E

Were you able to spy all of the correct answers?

Here are some pages of mixed questions which cover the different question types you've practised. If you get stuck, go back to the question pages to remind yourself how each question type works.

Try These

1. Anne and Lalla each make a snowman. Anne isn't happy with her snowman so she makes the changes shown on the right.

   Lalla, who copies everything Anne does, makes the same changes to her snowman. What will Lalla's snowman look like after these changes?

Anne's snowman

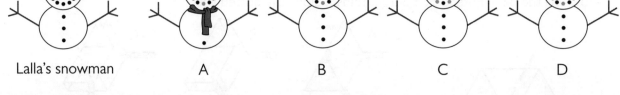

Lalla's snowman   A   B   C   D

2. Gareth folds a square piece of paper twice and then punches three holes in it, as shown below. On the paper on the right, draw where the holes will be when the piece of paper is unfolded.

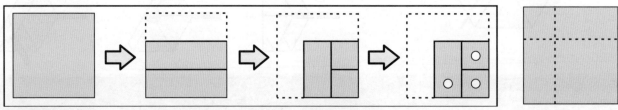

3. Elliott plans to build the car engine below using the engine parts on the right. Write letters next to the correct sides of the engine parts to show how Elliott should join them together.
   Sides that join together should be labelled with the same letter.

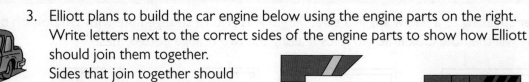

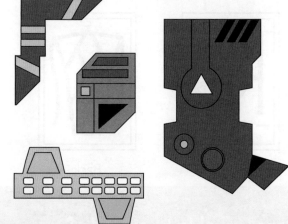

4. Mary and Yasmin see a water feature from two different positions.
The water feature is then switched off. Which option shows Mary's view of the water feature?
Which option shows Yasmin's view?

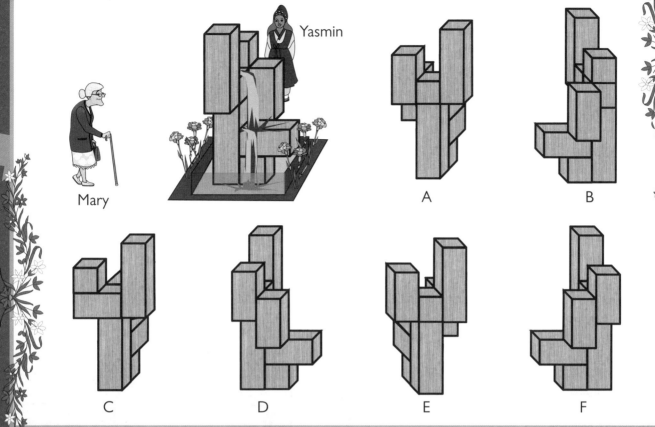

A   B

C   D   E   F

An Extra Challenge

An artist, Julian, draws five similar paintings. He names the first four paintings with the
code letters shown below. Julian then declares that the fifth painting is his masterpiece.
What will the name of Julian's masterpiece be in code letters?

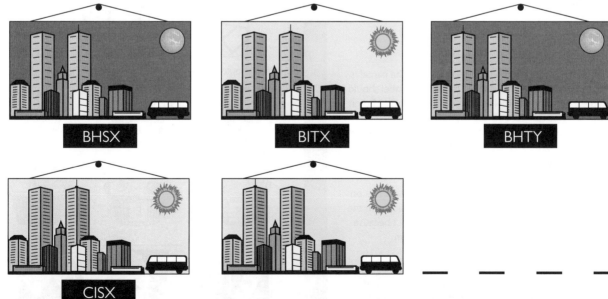

BHSX   BITX   BHTY

CISX

**Did you fly or fall getting
mixed up in it all?**

45

Answers

Pages 2-3 — Complete the Pair

1. **B**

   The rectangular part of the pencil is shortened and the pencil is rotated 90 degrees clockwise.

2. **C**

   Half of the top waffle disappears.
   The top waffle moves to the back.

3.

   The thick lines become dashed lines and the dashed lines become thick lines. The top button moves to the other side of the waistcoat.

4. **D**

   One burger turns black, one sausage disappears (Rodney's eaten it!) and any remaining sausages are rotated 180 degrees.

5. **A — X**
   B — Y
   C — W

   The middle flower moves from the back row to the front row. The other two flowers swap positions.

   ### An Extra Challenge

   The apple moves to the back and rotates 90 degrees anticlockwise. The strawberry moves to the front and its stalk is reflected across.

Pages 4-5 — Shaded Nets

1. **E**

   A is not correct because the label on the top of the parcel is in the wrong place. B is not correct because the label should be on the front of the parcel and the solid lines should be on the left. C is not correct because the solid lines should be horizontal, not vertical. D is not correct because the lines on the label are missing. F is not correct because the arrow on the 'This Way Up' side is pointing in the wrong direction.

2. **B**

   A is not correct because the face with the nuts should be on the left-hand side. C is not correct because the face with the pink sweets should be on the top. D is not correct because the face with the pink sweets should not be brown.

3. **A**

   B is not correct because the blue face should be dark gold. C is not correct because the top face should be silver and the right-hand face should be light gold. D is not correct because the front of the locket should be dark gold.

4. You should have labelled the net like this:

   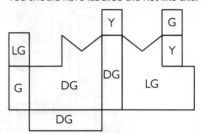

   ### An Extra Challenge

   C

   A is not correct because the two dark purple petals shouldn't be next to each other. B is not correct because the striped purple petal should be in the middle. D is not correct because the petal on the right-hand side should be solid dark purple. E is not correct because the petal on the right-hand side should be light purple.

Pages 6-7 — Hidden Shape

1. You can't see shapes **B**, **E** or **G**. The other shapes are here:

2. a) **D**

   b) **B and C**

3. You should have labelled the cupcakes like this:

4.

Answers

An Extra Challenge

Pages 8-9 — Rotate the Figure

1. **C**
   A and D have been reflected and rotated.
   The red light on B's chest has moved.

2. **A**
   C and D have been reflected and rotated.
   In B, the letters on the shuttle have been reflected.

3. **B**, **C** and **E**
   These three are the only options where all the shapes and lines
   are in the same place relative to each other as in the original.

4. **C**
   A has been reflected. B and D do not have parallel lines
   sticking out from the central, trapezium-like shape.

5. **A** and **D**
   B and **H**
   C and **F**
   E and **G**

   An Extra Challenge

   A, **E** and **F** are the correct cows.
   The lightning marks on cows B, C and D have
   all been reflected or shaded incorrectly.

Pages 10-11 — Cubes and Nets

1. **B**, **E** and **H**
   A cannot be made from the net because the burger should
   be on the right. C cannot be made from the net because the
   croissant and the drink can should be on opposite sides.
   D cannot be made from the net because the cupcake and the
   burger should be on opposite sides. F cannot be made from
   the net because the top of the drink can should point towards
   the teacup. G cannot be made from the net because there is
   no packet of crisps on the net.

2. **Luna** rolls **ice skating**
   Rotating the net 90 degrees clockwise means the football is to
   the right of the tennis racket and ball.
   Ahmad rolls **basketball**
   Rotating the net 90 degrees anticlockwise means the tennis
   racket and ball is to the right of the cricket bat and ball.
   Georgia rolls **tennis**
   Rotating the net 180 degrees means the ice skates are to the
   right of the football.

3. Cubes **A**, **B** and **E** are made from **Net 1**
   On cube A, the top of the fish is closest to the starfish.
   On cube B, there is a seahorse.
   On cube E, the front of the fish is closest to the bubbles.
   Cubes **C**, **D** and **F** are made from **Net 2**
   On cube C, the bottom of the fish is closest to the starfish.
   On cube D, there is an octopus.
   On cube F, the top of the fish is closest to the bubbles.

4.
   The point of the droplet is closest to the zigzag.
   The round end of the droplet is closest to the blue cross.

   An Extra Challenge

   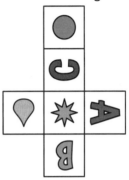

   From the first cube we know that A is to the left of B when B
   is viewed upright. From the third cube we know that the star
   is at the bottom of B, and the droplet is next to the star and
   pointing towards B. From the second cube we know that the
   round end of the droplet is next to the top of the C, and that
   the open part of the C points towards the green circle.

Pages 12-13 — Find the Figure Like the Others

1.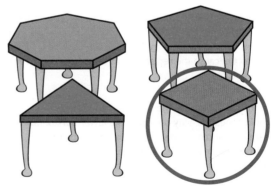

   The tables must have an even number of sides.

2. **A, C, H**
   The large outer shape must have more sides than the small
   shape inside it. The small shape must have a dotted outline.

3. **B**
   The pencil must point to the rectangle with the same line
   pattern as the rubber. The colour of the book should match
   the rubber and the rubber should be halfway up the side of
   the book.

4.

All the gingerbread people in the left-hand family have two matching buttons. The shapes of their eyes are vertical reflections of each other.

All the gingerbread people in the middle family have three buttons and eyes that are different shapes. Their top and bottom buttons must be the same colour as their right eye, and their middle button must be the same colour as their left eye.

All the gingerbread people in the right-hand family have two eyes that are the same shape and the same way up. Their buttons must all be different colours.

An Extra Challenge

begin

The letters in each word are in alphabetical order.

Pages 14-15 — 2D Views of 3D Shapes

1. **C**
   B and D are incorrect because there should be three squares stacked directly on top of each other in the centre of the figure. A is incorrect because there should be two squares visible on the left-hand side.

2. **C**
   A is incorrect because the green book should be on top of the pink book. B is incorrect because the green book is facing the wrong way. D is incorrect because the pink book is too short.

3. **D**
   A is incorrect because the arch should appear above a grey building. B is incorrect because the two towers are too close together. C is incorrect because the building in the bottom-right corner should be light grey.

4. **A**
   B is incorrect because the red and yellow sections at the top of the figure are too small. C is incorrect because the grey squares (the floodlights) are in the wrong positions. D is incorrect because the red section at the bottom of the figure should be grey.

5. **A**
   B is incorrect because the upper horizontal beam should appear directly on top of the lower horizontal beam. C is incorrect because there should be two horizontal beams visible. D is incorrect because there should only be two vertical beams visible.

An Extra Challenge

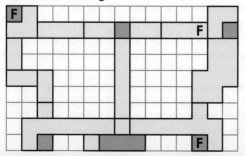

Pages 16-17 — Connecting Shapes

1. **B**
   A, C and E are ruled out because the trapezium should not connect to the blue piece. D is ruled out because the green piece should connect to the shortest side of the trapezium.

2. **D**
   A and C are ruled out because the small rectangle should connect to a long side on the L-shape. B is ruled out because the large rectangle should connect to the square.

3. The first set of shapes should be labelled like this:

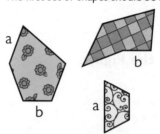

The second set of shapes should be labelled like this:

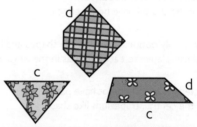

It doesn't matter which letters you used, as long as the matching letters are on the correct sides.

4. The pieces should be labelled like this:

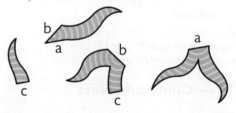

It doesn't matter which letters you used, as long as the matching letters are on the correct sides.

An Extra Challenge

The den should look like this:

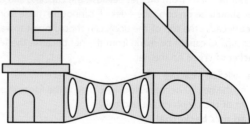

Pages 18-19 — 3D Rotation

1. a) **Victor** is right.
   Gemima's answer is a reflection of the correct answer.

   b) **Gemima** is right.
   The orange box in Victor's answer is in the wrong place.

Answers

2. You should have circled these pieces of food:

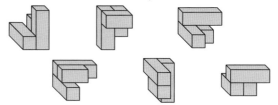

3. a) **Oscar's rock — B**
Oscar's rock has been rotated 90 degrees away from you, top-to-bottom. It has then been rotated 90 degrees left-to-right.
Opal's rock — D
Opal's rock has been rotated 90 degrees clockwise in the plane of the page.
Otto's rock — A
Otto's rock has been rotated 90 degrees towards you, top-to-bottom.
Olive's rock — C
Olive's rock has been rotated 180 degrees towards you, top-to-bottom.

b) **B**
B is rotated 90 degrees anticlockwise in the plane of the page, then 90 degrees right-to-left to give the stick in the box.

An Extra Challenge

B
To get A, the first piece of rubble is rotated 90 degrees right-to-left, then 90 degrees away from you, top-to-bottom.
To get C, the third piece of rubble is rotated 90 degrees right-to-left, then 90 degrees away from you, top-to-bottom.
To get D, the fourth piece of rubble is rotated 90 degrees left-to-right, and then 90 degrees towards you, top-to-bottom.

Pages 20-21 — Complete the Series

1. **C**
The frog's colours swap round and a spot is removed from its back each time.

2. **B**
This series is made up from two pairs of snakes. In each pair, the first snake is reflected over and the number of teeth increases by one to give the second snake.

3.

The small shapes on each banana change between spots and stripes. The main colour of each banana is the same as the small shapes on the previous banana.

4. **C**, **F** and **H**
The stripes on the tail go in the order: blue, green, white.

5. **B**
The trees alternate between small and large and go in the order: orange pine tree, oak tree, palm tree.

An Extra Challenge

The shape of the leaves goes in the order: diamond, irregular pentagon, six-sided arrow. The colour on the leaves goes in the order: yellow, orange, blue, green. The small shape in the centre of each leaf rotates 45 degrees anticlockwise each time.

Pages 22-23 — Reflect the Figure

1. **B**
In A, the green and red triangles are in the right places, but haven't been reflected. C is a rotation. In D, the colours are in the wrong order.

2. **D**
The letters in A have been reflected in the wrong direction. In B, the colours are the wrong way round. C has the wrong shape. E is pointing the wrong way.

3. **A — F**
B — C
E — G
D is therefore the odd one out — it is the only plane with coloured dots on different sides of its wing.

4.

5. **B**
The colours in A are the wrong way round.
In C, the red nose of the plane is the wrong shape.
In D, the large green section is the wrong shape.
E is a rotation.

An Extra Challenge

Miranda was reflecting in a horizontal mirror line because the green shape has moved from the top to the bottom. The reflection will look like this:

Answers

Pages 24-25 — Complete the Shape

1. **D**

   A and B are not correct because there should be four cubes at the front of the missing piece. C is not correct because the shape at the bottom of the missing piece should be on the left-hand side.

2. You should have circled these two pieces:

   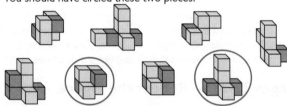

3. **C** and **E**

   C fits onto the left-hand side of the fireplace. E is rotated 90 degrees away from you, top-to-bottom. It then fits on the top of the fireplace. A is not correct because the grey cube should be on the left-hand side and the brown shape next to it should be three cubes long. B is not correct because there shouldn't be a light brown cube at the bottom of the figure. D is not correct because the dark brown cube should be at the bottom of the figure. F is not correct because the light brown shape should be on the left of the middle brown shape.

4. a) **B**

   You need to rotate B 90 degrees right-to-left for it to fit on the front left of the chunk of meat. A is not correct because it has too many cubes. C is not correct because the cube at the top of the shape should be attached to the left of the cube below it (and then it could be rotated 90 degrees right-to-left to fit). D is not correct because the cube on the back right of the shape should be behind the middle stack of cubes.

   b) **A**

   You need to rotate Sharky's second bite 90 degrees towards you, top-to-bottom, for it to fit on the back left of the chunk of meat. B and C are not correct because there should be two cubes on the left-hand side.

   An Extra Challenge

   You should have matched each experiment to these smashed pieces:

   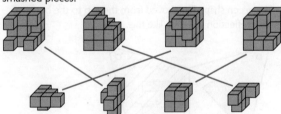

   If the broken off piece from experiment 1 is rotated 90 degrees right-to-left it fits on the front of the crystal.
   If the broken off piece from experiment 2 is rotated 90 degrees clockwise in the plane of the page it fits on the top of the crystal.
   If the broken off piece from experiment 3 is rotated 90 degrees towards you, top-to-bottom, it fits on the front of the crystal.
   If the broken off piece from experiment 4 is rotated 90 degrees clockwise in the plane of the page it fits on the front of the crystal.

Pages 26-27 — Prehistoric Adventure

1. **E**

   In A, the part of the paper that has been folded should still be visible. In B and C, the part of the paper that has been folded is the wrong shape. In D, the fold line is in the wrong place.

2. The coordinates are **E5**.
   The pattern looks like this:

   The series is made up of two pairs of figures. The lines shown in red are added to the first figure to make the second figure.

3. The pieces should be labelled like this:

   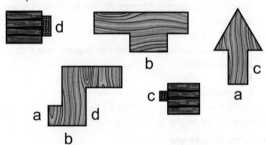

   It doesn't matter which letters you used, as long as the correct pairs of sides have the same letters.

4. **B**

   In A, the tree trunk is the wrong shape. In C, the big clump of leaves is the wrong way round. D is a rotation.

5. **D**

   In A, the triangles would overlap. In B, the striped rectangles would overlap. In C, the red and white striped rectangle would be on the bottom of the tent, instead of the side.

6. The dinosaur is here:

7. **A**

   There are ten blocks visible from above, which rules out B and D. There are two grey blocks visible in the front row, which rules out C.

Pages 28-29 — More Cubes and Nets

1. **C**

   A and B are wrong for a number of reasons. E.g. the third cube in A is not possible because the stalk on the cherry doesn't point towards a pear in any of the three nets. The third cube in B is not possible because the apple and the grapes are on opposite sides on all three nets.

2. **B**

   In A and C no half-faces meet up correctly. In D, there is no brown square next to the hair on a face square.

3. a) **Nets A, C and F make the same dice.**
    Nets B, D and E make the same dice.
    In B, D and E the cat and the snail are on opposite sides.
    This is not true for A, C and F.

    b) **Left-hand dice: snail**
    This dice is made from nets B, D and E.
    Right-hand dice: dog
    This dice is made from nets A, C and F.

An Extra Challenge

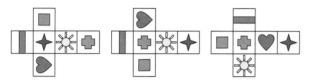

Pages 30-31 — Odd One Out

1. **A**
    In all other figures, the needle points between east and west.

2. **C**
    In all other figures, the stripe at the bottom of the hat is grey.

3. **D**
    In all other figures, the shooting stars are flying
    in opposite directions.

4. The odd one out for each type of object is circled below.
    The circled stamp is the only stamp where the head is
    behind the red lines. The circled scissors are the only pair
    of scissors with the lines on that side. The circled battery is
    the only battery with three different line types (solid, dashed
    and dotted).

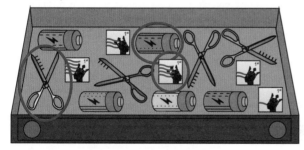

5. **D**
    On all other doughnuts, the sprinkles go in the order
    red-yellow-green clockwise around the doughnut.

An Extra Challenge

South
The bottom-right map is the odd one out.
In all the other figures, the giraffe silhouette has a tail.

Pages 32-33 — Fold and Punch

1. **C**
    Raymond's decoration unfolds like this:

    C
    Shazia's decoration unfolds like this:

    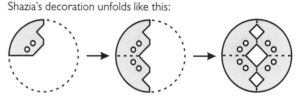

2. For the yellow piece of paper, you should have drawn the holes
    in these three places:

    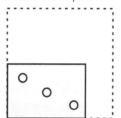

    This is how it makes the pattern:

    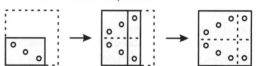

    For the pink piece of paper, you should have drawn the holes in
    these three places:

    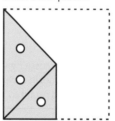

    This is how it makes the pattern:

    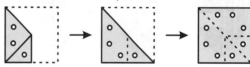

3. **A**
    The decoration unfolds like this:

    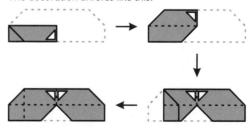

Answers

An Extra Challenge

The hidden word is **LIGHT**.
The unfolded paper will look like this:

This is how it makes the pattern:

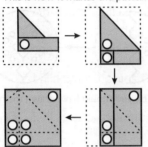

Pages 34-35 — Complete the Grid

1. **D**

    Working from left to right, a smaller counter is added on top of the existing counter(s). The new counter is the same shape and the same way up as the existing counter(s), but it is a different colour. The background alternates between white and grey.

2. **A**

    Working clockwise, the figure alternates between a lollipop and a sweet. The colour of the stripes on each sweet matches the colour of the spiral on the lollipop opposite. The lids alternate between yellow and green.

3. **D**

    The colour of the tile does not match the pattern in A. The dotted line in B is too high. The solid line in C is in the wrong place.

4. a) **A**

    The shield in the first column is reflected across to give the shield in the second column. The colours in each half of the second shield are then swapped round to give the third shield.

    b)

An Extra Challenge

In each column, working from the first piece to the second piece, the white shape moves to a different position on the edge of the large shape and a circle is added inside the large shape. Working from the second piece to the third piece, the white shapes disappear and a hole is cut out of the large shape. The hole is the same shape as the two small white shapes joined together.

The incorrect pieces are circled below.

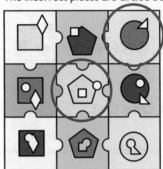

The top-right piece is incorrect because the triangle has been rotated. The middle piece is incorrect because the circle should be fully inside the large shape, and the square should be on the edge of the large shape.

Jasmine should have made them so they looked something like this:

On your green piece, the square can be in any position on the edge of the pentagon as long as it's not in the same position as before. The circle can be in any position inside the pentagon as long as its fully inside the pentagon.

On your pink piece, the triangle can be anywhere on the edge of the circle, as long as it's not in the same position as in the second row. The triangle must be the same way round as shown above.

Pages 36-37 — 3D Building Blocks

1. **D**

    A is on the left-hand side, partially hidden behind B.
    B is in the middle (the duck's main body).
    C is the orange block (the duck's beak).

2. **X — C**

    The top two blocks in C are positioned at the front of the figure. The remaining block in C is positioned behind these two blocks.

    Y — D

    The top-right block in D is at the back of the figure. The top-left block is positioned on top of it. The remaining block in D is positioned at the front of the figure.

    Z — B

    The left-hand block in B is at the front of the figure on the right-hand side. The remaining two blocks in B are positioned beneath it and behind it.

3. **A — 2**
    One of the blocks is used in the purple stand and the other is used in the green stand.
    B — 6
    Two of the blocks are used in the orange stand.
    Two of the blocks are used in the purple stand.
    One of the blocks is used in the red stand.
    One of the blocks is used in the green stand.
    C — 4
    One of the blocks is used in the orange stand.
    Two of the blocks are used in the red stand.
    One of the blocks is used in the green stand.
    D — 2
    One of the blocks is used in the red stand and the other is used in the green stand.

4. **A** and **C**
    B is ruled out because it is made from at least five blocks and the old wall only has 4.
    D is ruled out because if the block on the bottom right-hand side is from the old wall, then it must be either the L-shaped block or the vertical block that is two cubes high and one cube wide, and both these blocks are used on the left-hand side of D.
    E is ruled out because if the block at the back is from the old wall, then it must be either the L-shaped block or the vertical block that is two cubes high and one cube wide. It cannot be the vertical block as that is already used at the front of E. It also cannot be the L-shaped block, as then the bottom block in E would have to be L-shaped as well, and there aren't two L-shaped blocks in the old wall.

An Extra Challenge

a) **4**
    Their positions are highlighted purple on the front view below:

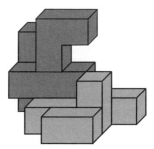

b) **Y** cannot be made.
    The block at the front of Y on the left-hand side must be D. Out of A, B and C, the block at the back of Y on the left-hand side can only be A. However, the block at the back of Y on the right-hand side can also only be A, so Y cannot be made.

Pages 38-39 — Codes

1. **KV**
    J = arrow pointing right, <u>K</u> = arrow pointing left.
    U = arrow in the middle of the rectangle,
    <u>V</u> = arrow at the top of the rectangle,
    W = arrow at the bottom of the rectangle.

2.
    L = not rotated, M = rotated 90 degrees,
    <u>N</u> = rotated 180 degrees.
    R = brown, <u>S</u> = pink, T = blue.

3. **ER**
    C = black shading, D = light grey shading,
    <u>E</u> = dark grey shading.
    P = vase with eye, Q = animal, <u>R</u> = weapon.

4. **CQY**
    B = lines above the shape, <u>C</u> = lines below the shape.
    P = hexagon, <u>Q</u> = diamond.
    X = two lines, <u>Y</u> = three lines.

5. **CRW**
    <u>C</u> = figures looking in opposite directions,
    D = figures looking in the same direction.
    <u>R</u> = different figures, S = same figures.
    V = background diagonal lines going down from left to right,
    <u>W</u> = background diagonal lines going up from left to right.

An Extra Challenge

 = not reflected downwards, = reflected downwards.

= 1 shape connected to triangle,

= 2 shapes connected to triangle.

= circles connected to triangle,

= squares connected to triangle.

Pages 40-41 — Different Views of 3D Shapes

1. **Muscle Man** sees view **C**
    There must be a vertical block three cubes high at the front of the figure. All the other blocks must be set further back.
    Dragon Dude sees view **F**
    There must be a horizontal block two cubes long which only touches the vertical block at a corner.
    The player sees view **B**
    There must be a block three cubes long at the top of the figure on the right.

2. **C**
    There must be a cube on its own on the left of the figure, which rules out A and D. There must be a long horizontal block at the bottom right of the figure, which rules out B.

Answers

3. **1 — E**

There must be three blocks in a stack at the front left. This rules out all options except B, C and E. There must be a vertical block two cubes high at the front right, which rules out C. There must be a cube at the back in the middle, which rules out B.

2 — C

There must be a cube at the front left, which rules out all options except C, D and F. The bottom block must be on the left-hand side, which rules out D and F.

3 — F

The bottom block must be in the centre, which rules out all options except D, F and G. There must be a cube at the back right, which rules out D. There must be a block three cubes tall at the front right, which rules out G.

4 — D

The bottom block must be in the centre, which rules out all options except D, F and G. There must be a cube at the back in the centre, which rules out F and G.

An Extra Challenge

C

A is ruled out because its right-hand leg is made up of two blocks, instead of three. B is ruled out because it has two blocks on the bottom at the back, and there should only be one. D is ruled out because the small pink blocks are attached to the wrong block.

Pages 42-43 — Fold Along the Line

1. **A**

B is ruled out because the part of the envelope that has been folded is too large. C and D are ruled out because the fold line has moved.

2. **D, F** and **G**

A, B and H will all unfold to give maps that are not rectangles. C and E will unfold to give rectangular maps that are longer than Sergio's map.

3. **D**

The left sleeve must be folded along a diagonal line, which rules out A. The right sleeve must be folded along a vertical line, which rules out C. In B, the fold line at the bottom of the coat is too low down.

4. **C**

The top left corner is folded over first, then the bottom left corner, then the top right corner.

5. **B**

A and D are ruled out because the fold line has moved. C is ruled out because the brown strap that has been folded over is pointing in the wrong direction. E is ruled out because the brown strap that has been folded over should still be visible. F is ruled out because the part of the parachute that has been folded over is too small.

An Extra Challenge

A

B is ruled out because the section that has been folded along the vertical fold line has the wrong pattern. C is ruled out because one of the fold lines has moved. D is ruled out because the sections that have been folded are too large. E is ruled out because the section that has been folded along the horizontal fold line has been rotated.

Pages 44-45 — Mixed Practice

1. **B**

The snowman's carrot nose is reflected across and every other stone making up the snowman's mouth changes from black to grey.

2. The unfolded paper will look like this:

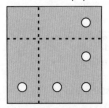

This is how it makes the pattern:

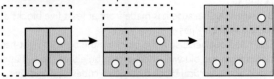

3. The shapes should be labelled like this:

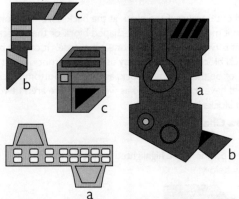

It doesn't matter which letters you used, as long as the matching letters are on the correct sides.

4. **Mary** sees view **A**

There must be a vertical block three cubes high at the front of the figure on the right-hand side, which rules out B, D and F. There must be a block at the back of the figure on the left-hand side, which rules out C and E.

Yasmin sees view **F**

There must be a vertical block three cubes high at the back of the figure on the right, which rules out A, C, D and E. The water feature is only three cubes long in both directions, which rules out B.

An Extra Challenge

CITY

B = eleven lines on each side of the two towers,
C̲ = twenty-two lines on each side of the two towers.
H = night-time, I̲ = daytime.
S = bus facing left, T̲ = bus facing right.
X = blue tower on the right and orange tower on the left,
Y̲ = blue tower on the left and orange tower on the right.